To _ANN_,

with lots of hugs

From _Gerry_   AUG-91-

©CARLTON CARDS, CLEVELAND, OH MADE IN U.S.A.

ISBN 1-56218-004-5

The Book of Hugs

Written by
Jo Ann Byrd

Illustrated by
Joan Jacobs Starcher

Hugs come in every shape and size
and mean so many things,
Like the hug that says,"I'm happy
for the joy your friendship brings"...

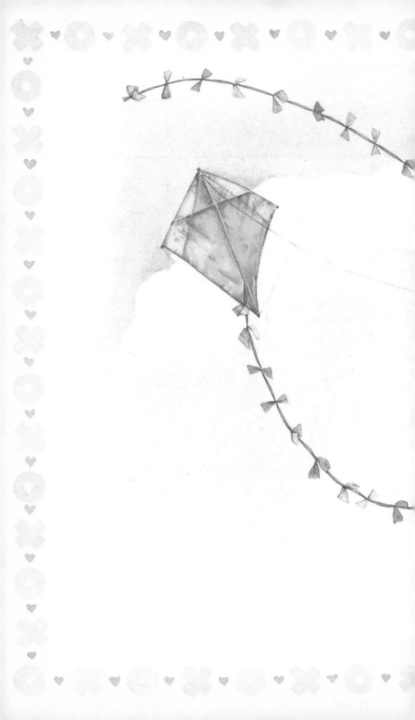

There are hugs for saying,
"I'm so proud
of all the things you do"...

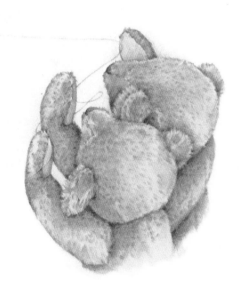

Hugs that say,
    "There's no one else
    in all the world like you"...

There are gentle hugs,
and tender ones...

...for feelings that are sad...

Hugs that say,
"I'm sorry,"
when someone's feeling bad.

There are happy hugs for saying,
"I'm glad you're here today,"
And ones that say, "I'll miss you
every moment you're away"...

And, of course, there are hugs
for making up
and showing you still care...

Very warm and special hugs
that more than two can share...

There are hugs for all occasions,
and reasons big and small,
Tiny hugs, and big bear hugs –
short to extra tall!

But the nicest hug
is one that says,
"I'm always thinking of you" –
The special kind
this brings your way...

The hug that means,
"I love you!"

(And I do!)
Nerry xxx
ooo